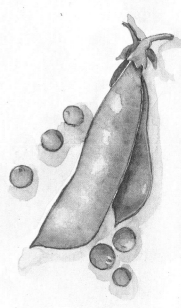

Published in Great Britain in 1989 by Exley Publications Ltd.
Published simultaneously in 1992 by Exley Publications Ltd in
Great Britain, and Exley Giftbooks in the USA.

12 11 10

Illustrations © Exley Publications Ltd, 1989
Selection & Design © Helen Exley, 1989
ISBN 1-85015-206-3

Printed and bound in Spain by Grafo S.A. – Bilbao.

Exley Publications Ltd, 16 Chalk Hill, Watford,
Herts WD1 4BN, United Kingdom.
Exley Giftbooks, 232 Madison Avenue, Suite 1206,
NY 10016, USA.

An illustrated

Cook's Notebook

illustrated by Juliette Clarke
and edited by Helen Exley

EXLEY

NEW YORK · WATFORD, UK

It was in France that I first learned about food. And that even the selection of a perfect pear, a ripe piece of brie, the freshest butter, the highest quality cream, were as important as the way the dish you were going to be served was actually cooked.

Robert Carrier

ravioli

farfalle

Penne

cappelletti

Beautiful soup! Who cares for fish, game, or any other dish? Who would not give all else for two pennyworth only of beautiful soup?
Lewis Carroll

We may live without poetry, music and art;
We may live without conscience and live without heart;
We may live without friends; we may live without books;
But civilized man cannot live without cooks.

Owen Meredith

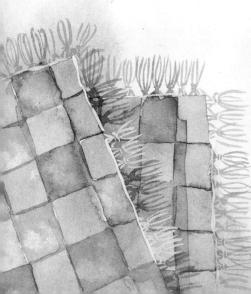

The whole Mediterranean, the sculpture, the palms, the gold beads, the bearded heroes, the wine, the ideas, the ships, the moonlight, the winged gorgons, the bronze men, the philosophers — all of it seems to rise in the sour, pungent smell of these black olives between the teeth. A taste older than meat, older than wine. A taste as old as cold water.

Lawrence Durrell

There is good dripping toast by the fire in the evening. Good jelly dripping and crusty, home-baked bread, with the mealy savour of ripe wheat roundly in your mouth and under your teeth, roasted sweet and crisp and deep brown, and covered with little pockets where dripping will hide and melt and shine in the light, deep down inside, ready to run when your teeth bite in. Butter is good, too, mind. But I will have my butter with plain bread and butter, cut in the long slice, and I will say of its kind, there is nothing you will have better, especially if the butter is an hour out of the churn and spread tidy.

Richard Llewellyn

The cook is a hand-craftsman, very much like a smith or a potter.

Nicolas Freeling

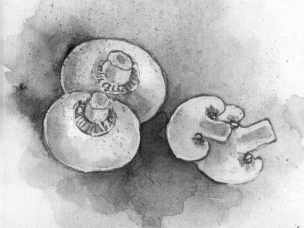

If pale beans bubbled for you in a red
earthenware pot
You can oft decline the dinners of
sumptuous hosts.
Martial, Epigrams Book XII

Cuisine is when things taste like themselves.

Curnonsky

*Noncooks think it's silly to invest
two hours' work in two minutes'
enjoyment; but if cooking is evanescent,
well, so is the ballet.*
Julia Child

God bless us all an' mak' us able
To ate all and stuff what's on this table.

Traditional

At a dinner party one should eat wisely
but not too well, and talk well but not too wisely.
W. Somerset Maugham

fenugreek

alfalfa

adzuki

mung

He who distinguishes the true savor of his food can never be a glutton; he who does not cannot be otherwise.

Thoreau

To eat is human; to digest, divine.

Charles T. Copeland

The smell of buttered toast simply talked to Toad, and with no uncertain voice; talked of warm kitchens, of breakfasts on bright frosty mornings, of cosy parlour firesides on winter evenings, when one's ramble was over and slippered feet were propped on the fender; of the purring of contented cats, and the twitter of sleepy canaries.

Kenneth Grahame

... an honest laborious Country-man, with good Bread, Salt and a little Parsley, will make a contented Meal with a roasted Onion.

John Evelyn

Parsley

Hamburg Parsley

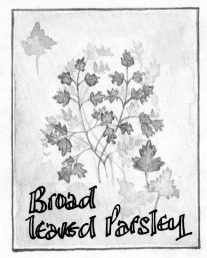

Broad leaved Parsley

I used to love the way everyone talked about food as if it were one of the most important things in life. And, of course, it is. Without it we would die. Each of us eats about one thousand meals each year. It is my belief that we should try and make as many of these meals as we can truly memorable.
Robert Carrier

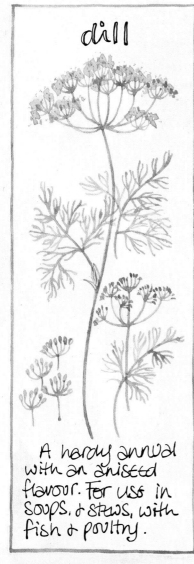

dill

A hardy annual with an aniseed flavour. For use in soups, & stews, with fish & poultry.

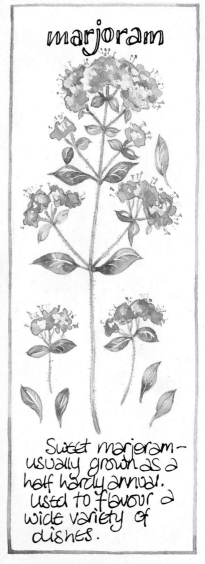

marjoram

Sweet marjoram — usually grown as a half hardy annual. Used to flavour a wide variety of dishes.

If a man be sensible and one fine morning, while he is lying in bed, count at the tips of his fingers how many things in this life truly will give him enjoyment, invariably he will find food is the first one.

Lin Yutang

I feel now that gastronomical perfection can be reached in these combinations: one person dining alone, usually upon a couch or a hillside; two people of no matter what sex or age, dining in a good restaurant; six people, of no matter what sex or age, dining in a good home.

M.F.K. Fisher

Let onion atoms lurk within the bowl,
And, scarce-suspected, animate the whole.

Recipe for salad

I am a pudding man. Nothing depresses me more than a meal which doesn't finish with one. "Just coffee for me, thanks," is not a phrase in my book. However boring the occasion, I perk up when they wheel in the sweet trolley.

I inspect it as I would a guard of honour. I insist the jellies should be standing to attention, the rhubarb, although I never touch it, pale pink, the chocolate sauce dark and mysterious. I look forward to the _petits fours,_ often nibbling the spun sugar in the swan's beak, or breaking off a piece of the basket and chewing the wickerwork.

Robert Morley

I detest minginess, cheating on quality… anything over-cooked, over-herbed, over-sauced, over elaborate. Nothing can go very far wrong at table as long as there is honest bread, butter, olive oil, a generous spirit, lively appetites and attention to what we are eating.
Sybille Bedford

There he got out the luncheon-basket and packed a simple
meal, in which, remembering the stranger's origin and
preferences, he took care to include a yard of long French bread
... some cheese which lay down and cried, and a long-necked
straw-covered flask wherein lay bottled sunshine shed and
garnered on far Southern slopes.

Kenneth Grahame

What I look for, in whatever country, in whose ever kitchen, are first rate materials – in season, fresh, cooked according to their nature with simplicity, skill and taste, presented with large-hearted ease, eaten at leisure, in the evening, mind at peace, with friends.

Sybille Bedford

In cooking, as in all the arts, simplicity is the sign of perfection.
Curnonsky

Wine makes bad food tolerable, indifferent food unnoticeable,
good food… well no adjective: those who know do know,
and those who don't would shrug. Good food
then __and__ good wine. And the better, the better.
Sybille Bedford

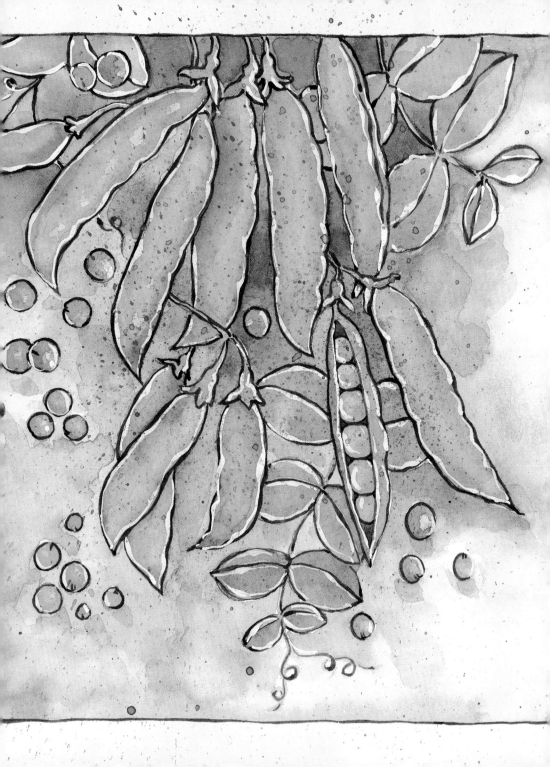

We are still on the chapter of peas... the impatience to eat them, the pleasures of having eaten them, the joy of having eaten them again, are the three questions which have occupied our princes for the last four days. There are ladies who, having supped with the King, go home and there eat a dish of green peas before going to bed. It is both a fashion and a madness.

Madame de Maintenon,
a lady to the court of Louis XIV

It is good for a man to eat thistles, and to remember that he is an ass.

E.S. Dallas,
writing about the artichoke, 19th Century

A crust eaten in peace is better than a banquet partaken in anxiety.

Aesop

It is wonderful, if we chose the right diet, what an
extraordinarily small quantity would suffice.

Gandhi

Doubtless God could have made a better berry, but doubtless God never did.
                                        William Butler,
                                about the strawberry

Pleasures may be divided into six classes, to wit, food, drink, clothes, sex, scent and sound. Of these, the oldest and most consequential is food: for food is the body's stay, and the means of preserving life. No other pleasure can be enjoyed, unless a man has good health, to which food is ancillary. It is not prohibited to take delight in food, or to occupy oneself and specialize in it, for indeed God says: "Say, who hath made unlawful the adornment of God which he brought forth for his servants, and the wholesome things of sustenance?" Likewise, whenever the Prophet was invited by any of his companions to partake of food with him which he had prepared to the best of his ability, according to his light, he did not refuse.

13th Century Muhammed ibn al-Hassan ibn Muhammed ibn al-Karim al Katib el-Baghdadi

No matter where I take my guests, it seems they like my kitchen best.

Pennsylvania Dutch saying

No artist can work simply for results; he must also <u>like</u> the work of getting them. Not that there isn't a lot of drudgery in any art — and more in cooking than in most — but that if a man has never been pleasantly surprised at the way custard sets or flour thickens, there is not much hope of making a cook of him.
Robert Farrar Capon

A cheese may disappoint. It may be dull, it may be naive, it may be oversophisticated. Yet it remains cheese, milk's leap toward immortality.

Clifton Fadiman

All millionaires love a baked apple.

Ronald Firbank

The kitchen, reasonably enough, was the scene of my first gastronomic adventure. I was on all fours. I crawled into the vegetable bin, settled on a giant onion and ate it, skin and all. It must have marked me for life, for I have never ceased to love the hearty flavour of raw onions.

James Beard

White Onion Red Onion

Spring Onions

Shallots

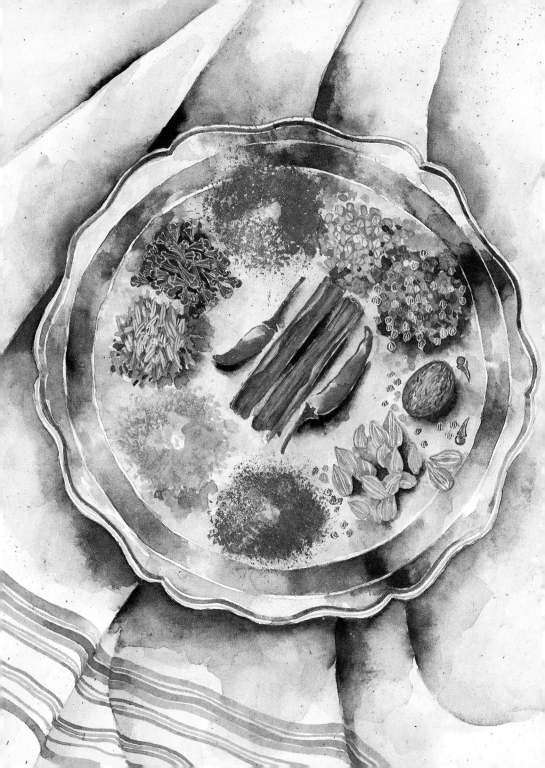

Woe to the cook whose sauce has no sting.

Chaucer

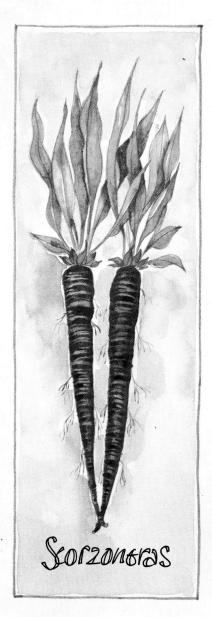

Scorzoneras

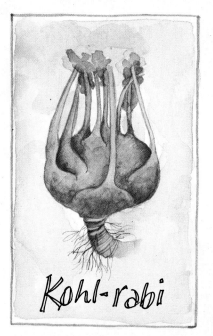

Kohl-rabi

Jerusalem
Artichoke

Every cook would be more imaginative if they were not catering for people!

Pam Brown

Any mother who has tried the experiment of adding interesting extra ingredients to a dish finds them in a neat pile on the side of an otherwise empty plate.

Pam Brown

O, blackberry tart, with berries as big as your thumb, purple and black, and thick with juice, and a crust to endear them that will go to cream in your mouth, and both passing down with such a taste that will make you close your eyes and wish you might live forever in the wideness of that rich moment.
Richard Llewellyn

*Part of the secret of success in life is to eat what you like and let
the food fight it out inside.*

Mark Twain

Grub first, then ethics.

Brecht

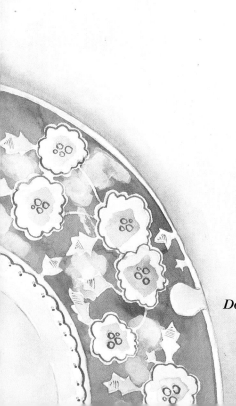

Don't let love interfere with your appetite.
It never does with mine.
Anthony Trollope

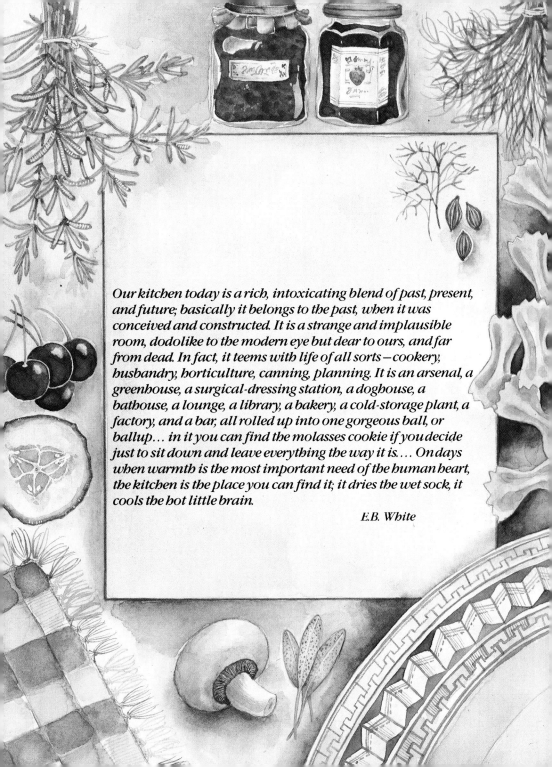

Our kitchen today is a rich, intoxicating blend of past, present, and future; basically it belongs to the past, when it was conceived and constructed. It is a strange and implausible room, dodolike to the modern eye but dear to ours, and far from dead. In fact, it teems with life of all sorts — cookery, husbandry, horticulture, canning, planning. It is an arsenal, a greenhouse, a surgical-dressing station, a doghouse, a bathouse, a lounge, a library, a bakery, a cold-storage plant, a factory, and a bar, all rolled up into one gorgeous ball, or ballup... in it you can find the molasses cookie if you decide just to sit down and leave everything the way it is.... On days when warmth is the most important need of the human heart, the kitchen is the place you can find it; it dries the wet sock, it cools the hot little brain.

E.B. White